Wild Bear

by Mary Beth Sampson
and Michael Sampson
illustrated by Julie Greig

Learning Media®

Wild Bear wakes.

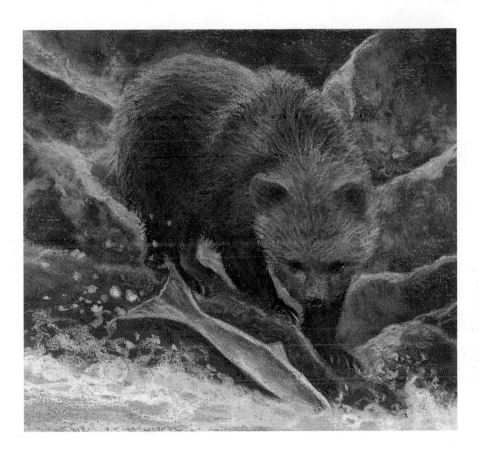

Wild Bear hunts.

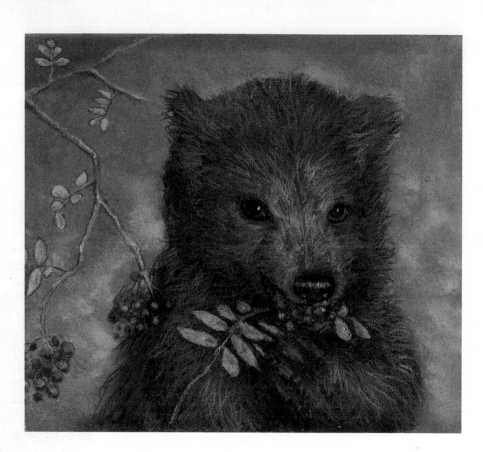

Wild Bear eats.

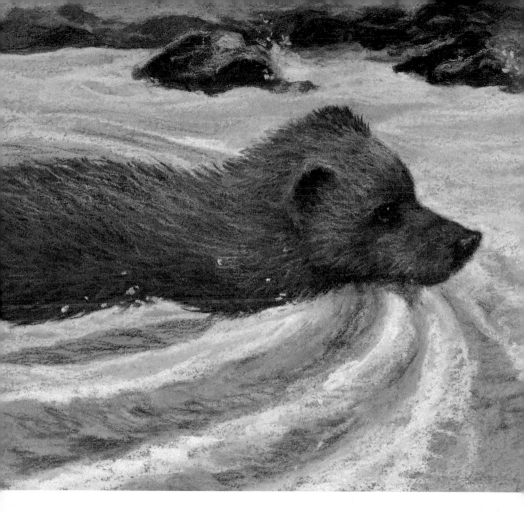

Wild Bear swims.

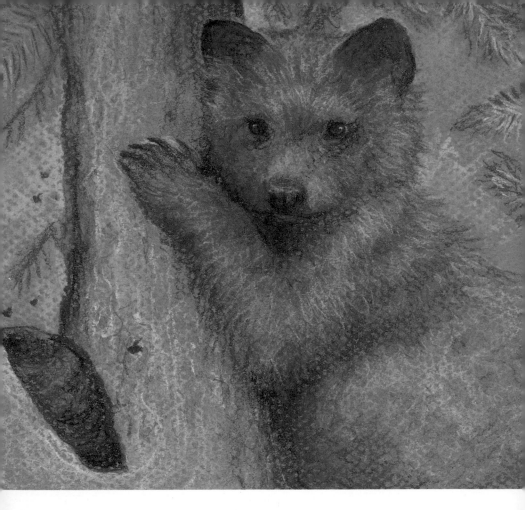

Wild Bear climbs.

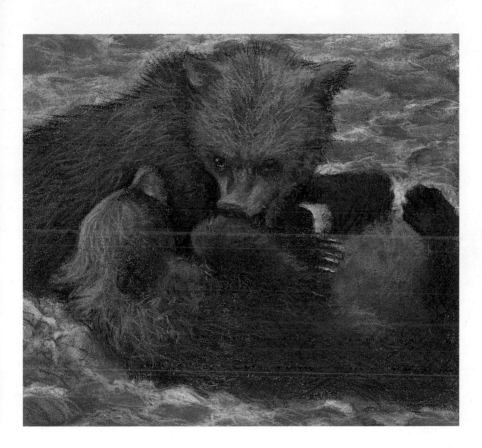

Wild Bear plays.

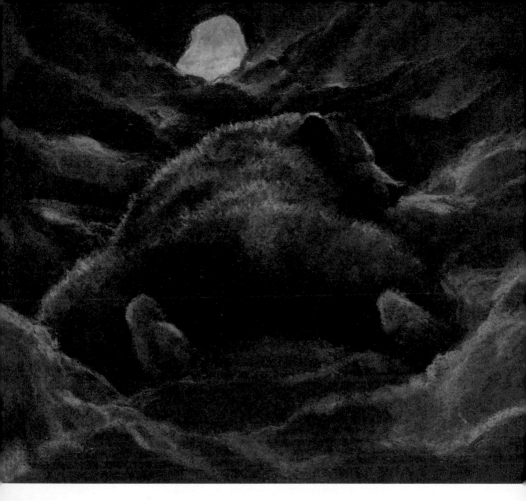

Wild Bear sleeps.